Be Amazing
Tools for Living Inspired

WORKBOOK

Includes a Guide to Starting a **POW WOW!**

Erin Ramsey

Be Amazing: Tools for Living Inspired Workbook

No part of this publication may be reproduced in any form or by any means, including scanning, photocopying, or otherwise without prior written permission of the copyright holder or publisher except for brief passages in connection with a review.

Printed in the United States of America

General editing: Connie Gorrell
Author photo by Daniel Knight, Studio B Photography

Living Inspired, LLC
www.erinramsey.com
In cooperation with OptiMystic Press, Inc.

ISBN-10: 0-9984438-1-6
ISBN-13: 978-0-9984438-1-2

This workbook is dedicated to my beloved POW WOWs!

The Original POW WOWs

Shari B.   Angie R.
Bambi D.   Becky T.
Jennifer D.   Holly W.
Kim N.

POW WOWS II

Barb F.
Leah S.
Vanessa W.
Connie M.
Deena G.

Living Inspired Lafayette: The Authentic Monkeys

The first group of women to come together because of **Be Amazing: Tools for Living Inspired**. Thank you experimenting with me.

Amanda G.
Melissa H.
Liz Nash J.
Elizabeth L.
Erin M.
Heather W.

To my husband, Doug, for welcoming all of the POW WOW's laughing, toasting, and crying every month for years in our home!

TABLE OF CONTENTS

Introduction

Living an amazing life does not need to be complicated, but knowing how to make it happen and actually doing it are two different things. This workbook is based on the book, **Be Amazing: Tools for Living Inspired**. It is intended to jumpstart your inspiration and encourage you during your path to *Living Inspired* as you move from knowing to doing. The tools in *Be Amazing* are simple and easy to use but require practice. The activities in this workbook provide strategies that will guide you in practicing using the tools. Each *Be Amazing* tool has three components: The Three Ps:

◌ Ponder

This is the section where you really make some time to think about the tool and how it is relevant in your life. This is where you look in the mirror. Make time to think in new ways and consider where you are and where you want to go.

✓ Practice

This is the section where you add to your reflection by doing something as practice in using the tool. This is where the rubber hits the road. This is your opportunity to walk the talk.

✵ Propel Yourself

This is the section where you set goals and plan action steps making this tool accessible in your everyday life in order to take you to the next level of being amazing.

This is <u>your</u> workbook so take your time. Focus on what you are willing and able to do so you set yourself up for success. Use colored pens, doodle, highlight and tab things. Have fun! Invite your friends to join you by starting a POW WOW! (See page 89, *Guide to Starting a POW WOW*)

CHOICE ONE

Embracing Self~Consideration

*Go out into the world today and love the people you meet.
Let your presence light new light in the hearts of others.*
                                            —Mother Teresa

Be Amazing Tools for Living Inspired Workbook

Be Kind to the Captain

Self-Consideration is not ignoring reality; it is reframing experiences so we can perpetuate self-love and learning.

Ponder

<u>When</u> do you most often talk negatively to yourself or experience self-doubt?

<u>How</u> do you feel when you talk negatively to yourself or feel self-doubt?

<u>Why</u> do you think you talk negatively to yourself?

What is self-doubt and negative self talk preventing you from doing? **What would you be doing if you were not afraid?**

✓ Practice

The next time I begin to talk negatively to myself or feel self-doubt I will:

- Use a word to stop myself.
  - ○ I will say:

- Visualize something to calm myself and chart a healthy course. Draw a picture.
  - ○ I will visualize:

- Ask myself questions for learning rather than judgment.

  - ✓ What do I feel good about today?

  - ✓ What would I like to have done differently?

  - ✓ What will I do or how will I respond next time?

  - ✓ Who do I admire? Who inspires me? What traits do they have that I would like to develop?

Practice Notes/Follow Up:

✵ Propel Yourself

Create a healthy and considerate bed time ritual.

1. Turn off the television or any other outside sources of stimuli.

2. Breathe deeply and identify ways to relax and get centered. *This could be calming music, a favorite lotion, a meditation, or a prayer.*

3. Think about your day and focus on what you *have learned*, who has *inspired you* and *what you are grateful for. You can go through this list on paper or in your mind.*

4. Focus on that for which you are grateful.

5. Use your practice strategies to avoid any negative self talk.

6. Tell yourself you love yourself right before you go to sleep.

Thoughts/Reflection/Practice Notes:

Write down your healthy and considerate bed time ritual:

I Am Not My Job

Self Consideration is letting your spirit guide you; not your roles.

💭 Ponder

What did you love to play as a child?

What do you truly enjoy doing now?

What does a typical day look and feel like for you?

What would an ideal day look and feel like?

✓ Practice

Practice noticing little things that you enjoy. Write down at least one thing every day for a week. Focus on small things that are totally doable.

This activity is intended to help you connect with yourself, create presence and figure out what you should create more of in your life.

Things I enjoy:

1._____

2._____

3._____

4._____

5._____

6._____

7._____

Practice Notes/More Things I Like:

> ### Erin's Favorite Simple Pleasures
>
> Fragrant candle
> New underwear
> Comfy pajamas
> Sun on my skin
> Good coffee or tea
> Nice cup to drink from
> Small water fountain
> Wind chime
> Fresh flowers
> Bubble bath
> Good book
> Magazine
> Long walk
> Nap
> Nature
> Special lotion
> Good playlist

✫ Propel Yourself

How can you reduce the gap in your life between what you love and what you are actually doing? What do you need to stop doing? What do you need to start doing?

STOP doing:

START doing:

I will use my natural gifts and talents by:

I will care for myself and stay connected to my spirit in the following ways:

Embracing Self Consideration

Not My Monkeys

Not my monkeys, not my circus.   —Polish Proverb

🗨 Ponder

How do I deal with people who create negative drama or people who are takers and not givers?

When am I depleted or drained by the people in my life?

✓ Practice

Who are the 3 people you spend the most time with?

Overall, how do you feel about the relationships in your life?

Family members:

Friends:

Colleagues/associations:

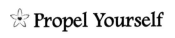 ## Propel Yourself

I want my life to be full of people who:

I want my energy and good will to create a circus of joy. I will do this by taking the following actions:

Embracing Self Consideration

Rewire for Good

By taking a few extra seconds to stay with a positive experience-even the comfort in a single breath-you'll help turn a passing mental state into a lasting neural structure.

—Rick Hanson

Ponder

List a few good facts about your life.

List a few good experiences you have during your daily routines.

✓ Practice

https://www.rickhanson.net

1. Look for good facts, and then turn them into experiences.
2. Really enjoy the experience.
3. Intend and sense that the good experience is sinking into you.

Record a time when you practiced these steps:

☆ Propel Yourself

Make Rewiring for Good a habit. Practice for a month. Record your good facts and how your life is changing by savoring them.

Notes and Thoughts about Embracing Self Consideration

AHAs

Feelings of Resistance

Bold Action

CHOICE TWO

Practicing Courage

Courage is the first of human qualities because it is the one quality which guarantees all others. —Aristotle

Pick a Word

Practicing courage means we are brave enough to take action to discover and pursue what we really want.

◌ Ponder

What do you want for your spirit? Not what you want for your loved ones, your bank account or your friends; what do you want for your spirit? Make a list of as many things that come to your mind.

.

Suggested Group Activity:

As a group, you can paint your word on a rock. You can use this rock to anchor yourself. If you want to go a step further, make list of what no longer serves you. Then as a group you can burn your list in a fire as you say your word to anchor yourself in what you want. See *Burn It Up!* in the Appendix, page 105.

✓ Practice

Pick one word on which to focus. Use your word as your guide.

When did you use your word?

How can you make your word more of a guide?

Did your word help you stay connected to what you want?

✻ Propel Yourself

Make decisions based on what you want rather than what you don't want.

Write or draw pictures of what you want more of in your life.

Bust through the Fear Barrier

Practicing courage is making the decision and taking action that can propel your entire life in a matter of minutes.

💭 Ponder

What are you afraid of? Make a list of things about yourself that are holding you back from what you really want. Give yourself time to think about this; be brave and honest. Don't beat yourself up. Just use a clear and gentle honesty with yourself so you can get to the place where you will shine the brightest for the benefit of others.

I am afraid of...

I am afraid that...

✓ Practice

Pick one thing you plan to do to address a fear. It could be to tell someone how you are really feeling; it could be to do something you are afraid to do, or something that you have self-doubt about.

Write down when, where and how you are going to *Bust through the Fear Barrier*. It doesn't really matter what it is; the most important thing is that you start to practice. Commit to being brave. Also, write down the worst thing that could possibly happen if you do what you are afraid of. Write down what the best possible thing is, too.

Afraid + Take Action = Confidence

Confidence + Inspiration = AMAZING!

Every time you do something you are afraid to do write it down here. Make sure you record the little things and the big things; everything counts when you are Practicing Courage. You will be amazed at how fast you will build your courage and it is super fun to look back at the list to remember and appreciate your bravery.

Practicing Courage

Wouldn't it be great if...?

When we know what we want and we ask for what we want we are opening the doors to be able to contribute more to others.

⌕ Ponder

When do you feel like you are living an amazing life? How do you feel?

Do you think you are inspiring others? Why or why not?

Are you happy and living your wildest dreams? Do you know what you really want?

Who inspires you and why?

> **Tips for *Wouldn't it be great if...?***
>
> Be outlandish
>
> If you feel crazy or scared then you are doing it right.
>
> Trust the process.
>
> Visualize what you want; not what you don't want.
>
> Practice Courage.

If you could spend more time doing three things what would they be?

1.

2.

3.

✓ **Practice**

Wouldn't it be great if:

Wouldn't it be great if:

Wouldn't it be great if:

Wouldn't it be great if:

Wouldn't it be great if:

Wouldn't it be great if:

Wouldn't it be great if:

Wouldn't it be great if:

Wouldn't it be great if:

Wouldn't it be great if:

Wouldn't it be great if:

Wouldn't it be great if:

Wouldn't it be great if:

Wouldn't it be great if:

Wouldn't it be great if:

Wouldn't it be great if:

Wouldn't it be great if:

Wouldn't it be great if:

Wouldn't it be great if:

Wouldn't it be great if:

Wouldn't it be great if:

✻ Propel Yourself

Once you compile all of the 'Wouldn't it be great ifs?' turn them into present and achieved statements. Write out your 'picture perfect' life as if it has already happened. Then record yourself reading it on your phone and listen to it often. You can also make a vision board and frame it.

How old will you be in 5 years? _____

In great detail with big and bold thinking write down your "picture perfect:"

Recommended reads to enhance this Tool: *The Millionaire Course* by Marc Allen, *The Secret* by Ronda Byrne, *and Life Visioning* by Michael Beckwith.

Notes and Thoughts about Practicing Courage

AHAs

Feelings of Resistance

Bold Action

CHOICE THREE

Creating Joy

Joy is the holy fire that keeps our purpose warm and our intelligence aglow.
                                                    —Helen Keller

Creating Joy

Break the Bad News Trance

Finding positive ways to nourish your mind creates joy.

💭 Ponder

How often do you watch, read or listen to negative news? How many hours a week?

When do you have the most exposure to negative news? What times of the day?

How many hours a week do you intentionally read, watch or listen to positive things?

> **Helpful Information**
>
> Books with research, strategies, biographies, or spiritual guidance
>
> Guided Meditations
>
> Documentaries
>
> Soothing or Happy Music
>
> Funny Videos
>
> Podcasts

✓ Practice

What can you have available to ensure you fill your mind with positive, proactive information?

How can you embed this type of information throughout your daily routine? When can you do away with negative information?

☆ Propel Yourself

Become super aware of what you are letting take up space in your mind, consciously and unconsciously. Nourish and protect your mind every day. It is essential that you stay away from negative news first thing in the morning and right before you go to bed.

What can do you do to take time in the morning to set your intentions for the day in a peaceful way?

What can you do to practice gratitude right before bed? This can enhance or align with your healthy bedtime rituals.

What other times of the day should you be careful about exposure to negative news?

Say YES with a Clean Heart

Saying YES with a clean heart is not a free ride to saying no to people and situation that have meaning and purpose; rather it is a ticket to stop saying yes out of guilt.

◯ Ponder

In what areas of your life are you doing things out of guilt or for the need to be accepted and for approval?

List the top five priorities in your life and why they are your priorities:

1.

2.

3.

4.

5.

✓ Practice

For the next few weeks, practice using these questions to guide your decisions and actions:

- ✓ Is this something to which I can contribute?
- ✓ Is this something that will help someone or something I care about?
- ✓ How will I feel if I say yes?
- ✓ How will this opportunity allow me to share my gifts and talents?
- ✓ Am I seeking acceptance from someone else or freedom from guilt by saying yes?

Write down an example of when you used these questions to guide your decision. Did you navigate in a new way? If yes, what did you do differently? How did you feel?

✶ Propel Yourself

Draw pictures or write words about what is most important to you. Create a visual tool that will help guide you when making decisions about what to spend your time on, who to spend your time with, and where to expend your energy. **Align your actions with your priorities.**

Creating Joy

Make Up Good Stuff

Save your bold energy for love.

💭 Ponder

What do you get really angry about?

How can you make anger productive by turning it into passion and action?

What are you willing to work hard for and be bold for?

✓ Practice

Pay attention to what gets you revved up and then turn it into something good. Write down your experience.

✿ Propel Yourself

Learn to be aware of where your energy is going. Decide where and how to use your energy.

Write down what you want to focus on instead of being bold in negative ways. How can you be bold in positive ways?

Creating Joy

Laugh on Demand

You can make your own funny; you don't have to wait for funny people or funny situations. Laughter is your spirit shining. Shine bright.

⌾ Ponder

Do you make laughter a priority in your life? Why or why not?

Write down one of the times in your life you laughed so hard you couldn't breathe and your stomach was hurting?

✓ Practice

Watch a funny movie. What did you watch? How did you feel?

Watch a silly video on the internet. What did you watch? How did you feel?

Go to the mirror and make fake laughing (Laugh on Demand) sounds until you start laughing. What happened?

Be brave and do Laugh on Demand with someone else. Who did you do it with? What happened?

✺ Propel Yourself

Share laughter at least 3 times a week.

Look for funny things when you are in a bad mood.

You are meant to live joyously!

How are things changing for you?

Creating Joy

Effortless Hospitality

You are a catalyst for joy.

💭 Ponder

When was the last time you invited someone to your home?

What prevents you from being hospitable? Make a list of everything that comes to your mind.

✓ Practice

Who would you like to reach out to? Think about people who you would like to get to know better and spend more time with. Why? What is it about this person or these people that you are drawn to? If you don't know anyone then write down characteristics of people with whom you would like to spend more time.

✫ Propel Yourself

Plan a gathering. Record what you are going to do and why. Write or draw the details of what you are going serve or offer, what you will do or talk about, how you will feel and how you hope others will feel because of your hospitality.

Notes and Thoughts about Creating Joy

AHAs

Feelings of Resistance

Bold Action

CHOICE FOUR

Being Compassionate

Love and compassion are necessities, not luxuries. Without them humanity cannot survive. —Dalai Lama

Everybody Has a Story

Compassion is when your heart sparkles.

💭 Ponder

When do you find yourself being judgmental of others? Are there certain situations or types of people that you are more likely to judge? Think about this and be honest. You need to identify it so you can change it.

What do you judge about yourself?

✓ Practice

List a few special things about you and your life, both present and past, which you have overcome. What are some things about your story that others may have judged without knowing you or the situation?

What can you do to help yourself refrain from judgment about others?

✫ Propel Yourself

Compassion for you is the foundation for compassion of others. How can you be more compassionate towards yourself? What are some areas of judgment that you can change? Draw a picture of what love for yourself looks like.

Plant Seeds of Love

By caring for another living thing we learn to better care for ourselves.

🗨 Ponder

What do you spend the majority of your time each day doing?

Who and what are you taking care of on a daily basis? How do you feel while you are performing the tasks of caring for others?

✓ Practice

Think about what you do in your free time. Choose something intentionally, with careful thought and a soft heart, to care for. It can be a plant, a pet, your skin, anything...just do it intentionally.   Write down what you are going to do and how you hope you will feel.

Write down what you did and how you felt using intentionality and compassion.

☆ Propel Yourself

When we are full of joy we have more energy. We are not hamsters on a wheel or walking zombies. Draw a picture or write down how you feel when you are intentionally planting seeds of love. Try to include more things you can do and think about it with intentionality.

Being Compassionate

Be an Instrument

You can make your life a masterpiece of contribution and love.

💭 Ponder

Look at your life right now. What song are you playing and what story are you writing with your daily actions and thoughts?

> **The Peace Prayer**
>
> *Lord, make me an instrument of Thy peace;*
>
> *Where there is hatred, let me sow love;*
>
> *Where there is injury, pardon;*
>
> *Where there is doubt, faith;*
>
> *Where there is despair, hope;*
>
> *Where there is darkness, light;*
>
> *And where there is sadness, joy.*
>
> *O Divine Master,*
>
> *Grant that I may not so much seek to be consoled,*
>
> *as to console;*
>
> *To be understood, as to understand;*
>
> *To be loved as to love.*
>
> *For it is in giving that we receive;*
>
> *It is in pardoning that we are pardoned;*
>
> *And it is in dying that we are born to eternal life.*
>
> *~ Amen.*

✓ Practice

What do you want your legacy to be? How do you want people to remember you and what do you hope they share with others about your life?

✫ Propel Yourself

How will you align your actions, decisions, thoughts, and relationships with your above legacy wishes? What do you need to start doing? What do you need to stop doing?

Notes and Thoughts about Being Compassionate

AHAs

Feelings of Resistance

Bold Action

CHOICE FIVE

Living in Gratitude

Gratitude bestows reverence, allowing us to encounter everyday epiphanies, those transcendent moments of awe that change forever how we experience life and the world.
—John Milton

Reframe to Become a Waterfall of Appreciation

We build courage, connections, self-confidence, and strategies to share, compassion and resiliency through hardships. These are some of the greatest gifts for which to be grateful.

☁ Ponder

Write down one or two things that have happened in your life that seemed terrible and were extremely difficult but now you are grateful they happened. Write down why you are grateful they happened.

✓ Practice

Make a list of **50** things you are grateful for-visualize this list as a waterfall of gifts to guide you. Every little thing counts.

✫ Propel Yourself

We can train our minds to see more than we are feeling. How are you going to *choose* to define your experiences from a place of abundance? Be specific in strategies you will use to remember appreciation.

Gratitude Spot

It doesn't matter where your gratitude spot is; what matters is that you create time and space to really focus on gratitude and correlating it within a space to reinforce the likelihood you will continue to practice daily.

☁ Ponder

How many times a day do you think about what you are grateful for?

When are you most likely to have feelings of gratitude?

✓ Practice

Choose a spot where you are likely to be every day. It can be your car, kitchen table, bed or shower. Begin practicing thinking about what you are grateful for there. Do this every day for a week.

✩ Propel Yourself

Set up a special place just for you that you can have very own 'gratitude spot'. You can put positive reading material, special momentums, photos, spiritual practice tools and a candle or chime. Create a daily ritual in your special spot for gratitude. Write down where, how and what you are going to do.

Suggested Group Activity: Take a photo to share or invite your group over to see your special spot.

Celebrate Your Happy Story

It is the people who can use adversity for strength and move ahead with a focus on the good that will shine the brightest.

🗨 Ponder

What do you usually focus on when you think about your past hardships? List two of the negative things you refer to from the past that are a big part of your story.

Do you usually focus on happy memories or memories that are sad and difficult? Why do you think your focus is where it is?

✓ **Practice**

For every bad memory and every story of hardship begin to think about a good memory and story of success. Take some time and break your life down in to 5 or 10 year increments and list all of the **good things** you remember about that time in your life.

✿ Propel Yourself

Retrain your mind so you can rewrite your story of good. Now take some time to break your life down in to the same 5 to 10 year increments and write down the **hardships and how you benefited from them.**

Bigger Fish to Fry

You are destined for greatness and gratitude is the fastest road to your destiny.

🗩 Ponder

Are there times when you feel bogged down by the people or situations around you? Write them down.

✓ Practice

Be aware of situations when you feel drawn into drama, gossip or ill will. Stay alert to those situations and people that are super negative or even jealous of your joy. Use the mental prompt: I have *Bigger Fish to Fry*.

Write down when and where you have or you may be able to use this prompt recently or in the near future. Being super aware is the first step. Stopping yourself from getting drawn in to negativity is the next step that is life altering toward inspiration.

✫ Propel Yourself

How do you feel when you are grateful and joyful? Who do you want to be around; what do you want to be doing? What do you feel you can make a difference about in your life with a laser focus on gratitude? Remember: *Living in Gratitude is in no way dismissing your hardships; it is only choosing where to put your focus. Do not confuse the two.*

Notes and Thoughts about Living in Gratitude

AHAs

Feelings of Resistance

Bold Action

CHOICE SIX

Focusing on Presence

Most humans are never fully present in the now because unconsciously they believe that the next moment must be more important than this one. But then you miss your whole life, which is never not now. —Eckhart Tolle

His Whole Face Smiles

Presence allows us to see the beauty in others, to feel the connections all around us. It is truly the greatest gift we can give to ourselves.

💭 Ponder

How often is your presence 'top of mind'?

Do you feel rushed, distracted, and stressed out often? What time of day and in which situations? Make a list.

✓ Practice

By listing the most stressful and distracted times of the day, you can make a plan to practice being present during those times. Think of strategies (breathing, a talisman, closing your eyes, saying a mantra, a visual cue, a sound, etc.) you can use during these times that will help you step back and get into the moment. Planning ahead of time will help you employ your strategies. Write down what you are going to do to come back to presence when you are rushing, when you are distracted from those you love, when you are crabby, and when you are worried.

✿ Propel Yourself

Think about times during your day when you can you use the following mantras: "See and feel what is now." If you are distracted and are not listening to others or yourself in the moment say, "This is the person I love; this is the moment I have".

Focusing on Presence

Make a Mantra

Mantras can help remind us that no matter where we are or how we are feeling things are always unfolding in our favor. The unfolding is the process, and everything is a process.

Ponder

What messages can you give yourself to align your thoughts with your *goals* and *desires*?

Practice

When can you practice using these messages?

✿ Propel Yourself

What do you want your first point of reference in your mind to be as you coach yourself to your best life? Write your favorite and most powerful mantra. Use it all day everyday if you need to. This is about choosing your thoughts and breaking bad thought patterns.

Open Arms, Deep Breaths and Heart Centered Hands

Use your body to your advantage; listen to it and let it help you manage your mind.

💭 Ponder

When do you commonly feel your body constricting from stress?

Where in your body do you feel the constriction?

How often do you feel ill or talk about aches and pains?

✓ Practice

Practice focusing on presence every day for a week. Once a day record when you notice yourself moving away from presence.

These are typical indicators: you are distracted and not listening, you're stressed out, you are rushing, parts of your body are tight and ache, you are annoyed, or you are worried. As you begin to notice, practice using your body to help you come back to presence or use your mantras from the previous tools. A few mind body connections can be to open your arms wide with your palms up and open your whole chest, or put both of your hands on your heart or put your palms flat together and center them on your chest.

Not Present: When and how did you feel?	What did you do to come back to the moment? Strategy to Focus on Presence

✿ Propel Yourself

Identify strategies for presence that work for you. Create habits throughout the day to guide you back to the moment.

Write down or draw what you will do during the following times of the day to make presence a habit:

Morning:

Mid-Morning:

Noon:

Early Afternoon:

Evening:

Night:

Be Interested, Not Interesting

When we stop making things about ourselves we become more interested in others which lead to the reciprocal connection that we all long for.

🗨 Ponder

In most cases, when you have a conversation do you know more about the other person or does the other person know more about you when it is over?

Do you prefer to listen or to talk? Why?

✓ Practice

Intentionally seek out to converse with someone. It can be someone close to you or someone you have just met. Engage in this conversation with the intention to fully listen. Write down what happened and how you felt.

✾ Propel Yourself

Be CURIOUS about everyone. Be curious about them with a loving kindness. Be sure it is not from a nosy place but rather a place to know and understand them.

What questions can you ask yourself about others to propel yourself to loving curiosity?

Idea Book versus To-Do Book

Empty your mind. Make space for ideas and possibilities. Plant the seed in your mind that you can generate new ideas.

⌁ Ponder

How often do you go to the store and run the list in your head over and over again but then get home to realize you didn't get what you went for?

How often do things slip through the cracks because you forgot; paying a bill, appointments, birthdays?

When was the last time you came up with an idea?

✓ Practice

Start writing down your to-dos and start writing down things you have thought about. Your thoughts do not have to be a lengthy diary entry. They can include a book you want to read, a quote you heard that you liked, an idea that crossed your mind, a desire that was fleeting, or something you enjoyed. Just begin writing down what you need to do and what special thoughts or ideas come your way. Practice for three days straight in any way you want; on a piece of paper, in your phone or in a journal. After three days, record how you felt and if anything was better or interesting.

☆ Propel Yourself

Get a journal or notepad to record your ideas and to dos. You can have one that is divided by to dos and ideas or you can keep two separate ones. As you begin writing down what you have to do and what you are thinking about (remember this isn't a diary; it doesn't have to be lengthy or cumbersome) notice how you are feeling, how you are functioning in response to the demands of your life and if you are noticing more beautiful moments and generating more ideas.

Record strategies you are going to use to empty your mind to create space for ideas.

Mini Meditations and Purposeful Prayer

Prayer is a platform to share what is on your mind. Meditation is a platform to clear your mind to receive answers. Both are necessary in the process of learning presence.

⚲ Ponder

How often do you incorporate prayer and/or meditation into your daily life?

Do you think you talk/ask more from your Higher Power or do you listen more?

What would you like to do more of listen or talk on your spiritual journey? Why?

✓ Practice

For the next thirty days, set two times a day to have quiet time to help you focus on presence. Write down when and what you plan to do each day.

✾ Propel Yourself

Make prayer and meditation an essential part of your day. Write down how you feel and what you will continue to do in order to talk and listen to guide your spirit.

Monthly Meditation Log

Prayer is when you talk to God; meditation is when you listen to God.
—Robinson

There is no right or wrong; just figure out how to get quiet and clear your mind. Use your breath as a focal point. You may not feel anything; your mind will wander or you may gain insight; just roll with it. Let your journey and process unfold with an open heart and open mind.

Record date, length and how you felt during meditation for the next month.

Notes and Thoughts about Focusing on Presence

AHAs

Feelings of Resistance

Bold Action

Be Amazing Tools for Living Inspired Workbook

Make IT Happen, Rosie!

We can be what we want to be by using the tools and making the bright choices to live inspired. Let's show up for ourselves and others. Let us create joy. Let us be considerate-be compassionate. Let's live in gratitude and practice courage. Let's be present. You can be amazing. Make IT Happen!

Write down what you are most committed to in making your life uncomplicated and amazing so you can make your greatest contributions.

A Guide to Starting a

POW★WOW

Power of Women Working on Wonderful

Going Beyond Bunco and Book Club

Be Amazing Tools for Living Inspired Workbook

How did the POW WOWS come to be?

In 2013, I was reading *Archetypes* by Caroline Myss as recommended by Oprah. During the process of reading the book and taking the Archetype quiz I became reminiscent of my youth when my friends and I would take the magazine quizzes about personalities, body types, auras and styles. I remembered how fun it was to do this with friends. We were thinking about ourselves, learning about others, laughing and being curious; all from rudimentary questionnaires.

As I continued to read Archetypes I started thinking how great it would be to have a group of friends that I could talk about the book with. I also longed to have a group that I could discuss the things that I have read, explored and learned about in other readings and explorations.

I had been in book clubs and I had been in a Bunco group (popular dice game once a month). Both of which were fun but I longed for something more.

I wanted to be able to talk about my biggest dreams, I wanted to hear what other women were dreaming of but might be afraid to share.

I wanted fun and intellectual interactions.

I wanted formality and commitment with light heartedness and vulnerability.

I did not want the conversations and focus to be on our kids' activities or their schools, or to be about places of worship, religion or fundraising.

I definitely did not want to gather in honor of any pyramid selling product.

I wanted it to be about each one of us as individuals taking time to study, grow and learn from content and from each other.

I wanted a place that women could focus on growth and experiment with new ideas and tools.

A place where we could share our challenges but our challenges are not the basis of the gathering; but rather shining bright!

I emailed a few friends. I was a bit nervous that they may not want to do it or that they may say yes out of guilt or think I was crazy. I chose friends that I felt were open-minded. Everyone I invited did not know each other nor were they necessarily my closest friends but I thought they would want to learn and grow. I think having a mix of people from different areas of your life with different interests and ages adds to the core focus of each person on a personal journey within a group rather than just a group gathering. If you are planning to start a POW WOW remember not to take it personally if it is not for everyone; selecting the right people for the group is very important. Avoid negativity, judgment or whining to contaminate the process.

If you are coordinating a POW WOW or joining a POW WOW it is important to focus on being a catalyst of growth and connectedness for others.

The POW WOWs are not to be about our roles; rather it is about our spirits. We need to help ourselves so we can help others.

What is a POW WOW? Who is a POW WOW?

(They are interchangeable; one can be a POW WOW and one can be going to a POW WOW.)

A POW WOW is a platform for women to empower each other and take personal time that is not a fundraiser, a sales pitch, a gathering not associated with family obligations, religious or community endeavors. It is strictly for women to share, learn and grow together. POW WOW is the Power of Women Working on Wonderful. The premise of the POW WOW journey is that when women find their brightest light everyone benefits. The ultimate goal is greater contribution through practicing courage, embracing self consideration, creating joy, focusing on presence, living in gratitude and being compassionate.

Purpose of the POW WOWs:

- Learn about and use tools and practices to help live the life you have imagined; dreaming big and being brave.
- Create a network of constructive, healthy friendships for contribution, growth and personal empowerment.

Who should join? Someone who is:

- Open-minded who wants to experience personal growth.
- Longing for greater authentic connection with themselves and others.
- Willing to discover and work toward their greatest contributions and is willing to be courageous.
- Non-judgmental and willing to commit to the activities, meetings and to the people in the group.

What does a POW WOW look like?

- On average, a monthly meeting with 6-8 women and lasts between 2-4 hours (varies on topic and group).
- Casual and party like but a strong focus on the assignments and accountability.
- Homework assignments vary but usually include reading or writing.
- Group decides monthly contribution to be used for annual retreat.

Tips for Getting Started

Make a list of people to invite.

They do not all have to be your closest friends. The most important thing is that they are *open-minded* and that you are clear with them on the commitment and activities. Make sure you talk about courage and growth. Stay away from people who are negative and judgmental. They may be able to join once the group is established but not in the beginning. The whole idea is to help each other grow in a safe place; you don't want to compromise that with the wrong type of people.

Decide where to host it.

I suggest you keep it consistent for people to get comfortable and things are predictable until the group is well established before alternating locations. It should feel like a party and school all wrapped in one.

I started mine at my dining room table every month. If possible, the comfort and intimacy of a private area may lend itself to more conversations and less distractions than in a public place. Either is fine but it is important to pay careful attention to the details and the opportunities to support meaningful and focused interactions.

Be clear on the work.

You will want to avoid the tendency for groups to go towards surface fun activities away from the purpose of the POW WOW of *learning and fun*. Suggest everyone purchase a journal to track their assignments and/or use the *Be Amazing Workbook* for assignments. Beginning with the *Be Amazing book and workbook* might make the process easier for planning and growing. Once the group works through the book and workbook they will know each other well and can start to offer topics they are interested in, share hobbies, and suggest areas of study.

Go with the flow but don't get loosey-goosey.

If community events that are pertinent come up or other ideas surface be fluid and let the group decide together what the next meeting is. As long as everyone is committed and growing there are no rules.

Get to know each other right away.

The first meeting is to get to know one another and set the climate by assigning everyone to read *Archetypes* by Caroline Myss and take the archetypes quiz. At the meeting, everyone can share their archetypes. This is a great way to get to know one another in a fun, light way.

Group decisions.

You can add POW WOWs as the group progresses but the group needs to make the decision together before inviting anyone new.

Share food and drink.

If you are hosting in a home, each person brings an appetizer and what they would like to drink. Your group can handle this any way you would like but this worked well for me so no one is bogged down with the cooking on a regular basis. Again, your group can talk it through and decide but eat together because it is part of being in a community/family.

Facilitate so everyone participates.

The discussion of the assignments should be facilitated in manner where everyone shares their experiences, feelings or goals. There should be a guide to prompt each person to share as the discussions unfold naturally. This way those that are quiet will share and those that talk more will listen.

Leadership is needed.

If you are the coordinator and convener be prepared to keep everyone on target by sending emails and texts about the assignments, meeting times, etc. It does take some time and you are setting the tone. You don't want to let it turn into just a gathering; it needs to be a **learning experience** and a **fun gathering.**

Accountability is essential.

If you are a member you need to be sure to respond to communications, read and study and do the assignments. Get the date on your calendar and make it a priority to attend. <u>Attendance is required</u>. In order for this POW WOW to help you and you help others you need to show up.

Continual contributions.

Share interests and ask for input on things to study.

Commitment is important.

It is ok for people not to like or believe in every activity, topic or assignment. It should be a safe place to disagree but it is not alright to skip the work. It is amazing how much people have to share that they never had the platform to do share before; their fears and dreams.

Plan an annual celebration.

You can have a member be the treasurer and collect money (the group decides; probably around $10 to $20) at each meeting to save for annual trip or retreat. Collecting is optional but plan some type of annual celebration no matter what.

Sign the POW WOW Commitment.

Have everyone sign the POW WOW Commitment at the first meeting. Take time to discuss each of the commitments and decide if you your group would like to add any. (See Appendix)

A Year of Suggested Monthly POW WOWs

Month One: Get to Know Each Other

- Share archetypes by taking the free quiz at **www.archtypeme.com** and/or read *Archetypes* by Caroline Myss.
- Each person share why they decided to join the POW WOW and what they hope to give and hope to receive as a member.
- Each person share a little about their life story and their current reality.
- Set up plans for monthly meeting times, retreat fund, expectations, etc.
- Set assignment/discussion topic for next meeting.
- Review and discuss the POW WOW Commitment (See page 107 in the Appendix)

Month Two: Embracing Self Consideration

- Discuss the *Be Kind to the Captain* Workbook pages and everyone share in detail their new Healthy Bedtime Rituals.
- Talk about the changes, feelings and challenges of releasing negative self talk and doubt.

Month Three: Embracing Self Consideration

- Discuss *I Am Not My Job* workbook pages; focus on sharing things each POW WOW enjoys to help others get ideas of things to try.
- Discuss in detail the *Not My Monkeys* Workbook pages. Focus on strategies and feelings.

Month Four: Practicing Courage

- Discuss and share the *Pick a Word* activity. Everyone should bring a rock and paint their word on it at the POW WOW.
- Optional: *Burn It Up* activity (see page 105 in the Appendix). If you do this hold the rock in one hand and throw the list of what no longer serves you

into the fire while saying your word out loud. People can choose to read their list out loud but this should not be expected because it may be way too personal.

Month Five: Practicing Courage

- Discuss and share the *Wouldn't It Be Great If...* workbook pages.
- Focus on thinking big and being outlandish. The POW WOWs can help each other be brave and share big thoughts and dreams.

Month Six: Practicing Courage

- Each POW WOW reads their 'picture perfect' life out loud from the propel section of *Wouldn't It Be Great If...*.
- Each POW WOW shares their Vision Board with the group.
- Optional: Read *The Millionaire Course* by Marc Allen.

Month Seven: Creating Joy

- Discuss the *Break the Bad News Trance* Workbook pages.
- Focus on feelings of limiting the news and strategies to fill your mind with healthy things.

Month Eight: Creating Joy

- Discuss the workbook pages on *Say YES with a Clean Heart;* each POW WOW should share what their priorities are and what changes they have made or will make to ensure they are living in alignment.

Month Nine: Being Compassionate

- Discuss the *Everybody Has a Story* Workbook pages; focus on the propel section and share pictures of how each POW WOW plans to be more compassionate with themselves.

Month Ten: Being Compassionate

- Review the *Be an Instrument*; everyone can share what they want their legacy to be.

Month Eleven: Living in Gratitude

- Work through the *Gratitude Spot* activity. Everyone should bring a photo of their Gratitude Spot and share how they are creating space in their life to live in gratitude.

Month Twelve: Focusing on Presence

- Focus on the *Make a Mantra* section and everyone can share their mantras and how they are using them to stay present.

All of the activities in this workbook can be shared and discussed in any order your POW WOW decides. You can work through the tools year after year together because growth is a process. You can also insert various topics, books, activities, field trips or guest speakers as your group grows together.

POW WOWs Share Their Thoughts

I love being a POW WOW because of the connections I have made with amazing, positive, strong women. I also love that the POW WOWs provide a regular opportunity for me to actively and intentionally focus on my personal growth. It is a life changing opportunity to invest in yourself and others in a truly meaningful way. I want to see the world become a more joyful place and I am confident that this movement will facilitate joy!!
~ Vanessa W.

I decided to join a POW WOW because of the empowerment I feel from other women. It is so helpful in strengthening my courage and self-esteem. I love being a POW WOW because I have such support and can offer support to my POW WOW sisters because we have each other's best interests at heart.
~Bambi D.

I decided to join a POW WOW because I needed to make time for me so that I could think, reflect, support myself and other women in an environment built on joy, love and authentic relationships. I love being a POW WOW because it is a soothing space where even the introverted can realize their voice. The most challenging and joyous part of being a POW WOW is the journey of discovery. I discover, again and again, that I have within me everything I need! I just have to listen, be open and believe!!!
~Kim N.

I decided to join a POW WOW because I felt like I needed to carve out time in my busy life to take care of myself. It sounded fun and I wanted to make friends with some cool women outside of work. The sharing and learning together is incredibly uplifting. Even when what is being shared is sad or when what is being learned is challenging, the experience of sharing and learning together is so powerful and rewarding. I hope other people decide to join this movement because in a world where women like me spend two hours online researching and reading reviews before purchasing a new blender and only a fraction of that energy and effort thinking about what brings us joy—real joy—POW WOWs give much needed balance and intentionality to things that matters most.
~Jennifer D.

I hope other people decide to join this movement because POW WOW's are amazing!!! This is exactly what women, mothers, wives need! Even though it is sometimes challenging to feel comfortable with doing something for myself, I am committed to being a POW WOW because I have functioned in survival mode for a long, long time. Now, to actually start thinking about ME and putting myself at the top of the priority list is uncomfortable at times. It feels selfish at times but now I am acting on my dreams instead of just thinking about them!!   ~Leah S.

After my youngest child went to college I went through a year or two of seeking to redefine myself and found that I was in need of connection. I needed conversation with people who challenged me, accepted me and were challenging and accepting themselves. After hearing Erin speak about this book at a local conference, I felt that I had found the key to the connection I was seeking. I invited friends to join me in a conversation about living inspired.
~Heather W.

It is easier to remember and put into practice the goals I have set from reading the book. I share successes and failures with the others while moving forward in my goals.   ~Melissa G.

The POW WOWs feed my soul. I am accepted, encouraged and supported by phenomenal women who have become my closest friends. Having the opportunity to learn and grow with my POW WOWs is one of my greatest blessings!   ~Becky K.

Since studying the tools in Be Amazing I feel I have become reacquainted with myself.   ~Elizabeth L.

APPENDIX

BURN IT UP!

I no longer need the following in my life; they no longer serve me:

I have learned from the things on this page and now it is with gratitude that I say good-bye. By saying good-bye I know I will shine a little brighter and be closer to making my greatest contributions. I am on the path and committed to Living Inspired.

With love and optimism,

_____

Signature and Date

POW WOW Commitment

Power of Women Working on Wonderful

_____ I will be respectful to everyone in the group even when I disagree.

_____ I will be brave and share my thoughts, feelings, dreams and challenges.

_____ I understand that everyone is busy and time is valuable. I will commit to showing up for meetings even if it means I need to rearrange my schedule. I will put forth effort to show up. Going to a POW WOW once a month will be top on my priority list because I value this opportunity in my life and I want to support others.

_____ I will study and actively complete the assignments. I will be prepared and treat each meeting as a gift and a unique opportunity to grow and connect.

_____ I will actively listen to each person with an open mind and an open heart.

_____ I will never gossip or whine at a POW WOW. I will share my experiences and challenges with a focus on solutions and understanding; not complaining.

_____ I will be careful not to offer too much advice or high jack conversations.

_____ I will be careful not to withdraw or retract from participation if I am feeling uncomfortable or scared.

Signature   Date

Be Amazing Tools for Living Inspired Workbook

Yearly Reflection Tool

What are you most proud of from this past year?

What are some hardships you experienced that you have turned into your favor, grown from or managed well?

What are some hardships/challenges you experienced that you are still holding on to?

What goals did you set and achieve?

What are the top 3 most important things you learned?

What was unexpected?

What do you wish you would have done differently?

What do you most want to remember?

Start thinking about what you want to be able to say at the end of next year...

Living Inspired

Have Erin come speak with your group!

Erin offers keynote addresses, retreats and workshops. You can visit her website: **www.erinramsey.com** for popular topics. Each engagement is tailored to meet the needs of the group.

Contact Erin if you are interested: erin@erinramsey.com

Email photos of your POW WOW and Erin will add them to the Facebook page!

Living Inspired Products

Shop for Living Inspired books, candles, apparel and accessories on Erin's website. **Visit www.erinramsey.com/shop**.

Connect with Erin on Social Media:

www.facebook.com/ErinRamseyJoy

POW WOW Facebook Group:
www.facebook.com/LivingInspiredPOWWOW

Twitter: erinramseyjoy

Instagram: erinramseyjoy

ABOUT THE AUTHOR

ERIN RAMSEY

Erin Ramsey is a nationally recognized inspirational speaker with over twenty years of service in the public sector. She earned a Bachelor of Arts degree in Child Development and Psychology and a Master of Sciences in Public Service Administration.

Erin is married to her high school sweetheart and is the mother of three sons and a daughter. She loves to read, walk labyrinths, entertain and bring people together for empowerment.

Visit **www.erinramsey.com** to follow Erin's blog, order *Living Inspired* products or to connect with her on social media. If you are interested in inviting Erin to facilitate a retreat, a keynote address, a workshop, or strategic planning session, she can be reached at: erin@erinramsey.com. She would love to hear what you are doing to *Be Amazing!*

Made in the USA
Columbia, SC
10 December 2022

72733131R00067